FRANCIS FRITH'S
NOSTALGIC BRITAIN

ADDRESS BOOK

First published in the United Kingdom in 2003 by
The Francis Frith Collection

ISBN 1-85937-682-7

The Francis Frith Collection
Frith's Barn, Teffont,
Salisbury, Wiltshire SP3 5QP
Tel: +44 (0) 1722 716 376
Email: info@francisfrith.co.uk
www.francisfrith.co.uk

Printed and bound in China

FRANCIS FRITH, Victorian founder of the world-famous photographic archive, was a complex and multi-talented man. A devout Quaker and a highly successful Victorian businessman, he was philosophic by nature and pioneering in outlook.

By 1855 he had already established a wholesale grocery business in Liverpool, and sold it for the astonishing sum of £200,000, which is the equivalent today of over £15,000,000. Now a multi-millionaire, he was able to indulge his passion for travel. As a child he had pored over travel books written by early explorers, and his fancy and imagination had been stirred by family holidays to the sublime mountain regions of Wales and Scotland. 'What a land of spirit-stirring and enriching scenes and places!' he had written. He was to return to these scenes of grandeur in later years to 'recapture the thousands of vivid and tender memories', but with a different purpose. Now in his thirties, and captivated by the new science of photography, Frith set out on a series of pioneering journeys up the Nile and to the Near East that occupied him from 1856 until 1860.

INTRIGUE AND EXPLORATION

These far-flung journeys were packed with intrigue and adventure. In his life story, written when he was sixty-three, Frith tells of being held captive by bandits, and of fighting 'an awful midnight battle to the very point of surrender with a deadly pack of hungry, wild dogs'. Wearing flowing Arab costume, Frith arrived at Akaba by camel seventy years before Lawrence of Arabia, where he encountered 'desert princes and rival sheikhs, blazing with jewel-hilted swords'.

He was the first photographer to venture beyond the sixth cataract of the Nile. Africa was still the mysterious 'Dark Continent', and Stanley and Livingstone's historic meeting was a decade into the future. The conditions for picture taking confound belief. He laboured for hours in his wicker dark-room in the sweltering heat of the desert, while the volatile chemicals fizzed dangerously in their trays. Back in London he exhibited his photographs and was 'rapturously cheered' by members of the Royal Society. His reputation as a photographer was made overnight.

VENTURE OF A LIFE-TIME

Characteristically, Frith quickly spotted the opportunity to create a new business as a specialist publisher of photographs. He lived in an era of immense and sometimes violent change. For the poor in the early part of Victoria's reign work was exhausting and the hours long, and people had precious little free time to enjoy themselves. Most had no transport other than a cart or gig at their disposal, and rarely travelled far beyond the boundaries of their own town or village. However, by the 1870s the railways had threaded their way across the country, and Bank Holidays and half-day Saturdays had been made obligatory by Act of Parliament. All of a sudden the ordinary working man and his family were able to enjoy days out and see a little more of the world.

With typical business acumen, Francis Frith foresaw that these new tourists would enjoy having souvenirs to commemorate their days out. In 1860 he married Mary Ann Rosling and set out on a new career: his aim was to photograph every city, town and village in Britain. For the next thirty years he travelled the country by train and by pony and trap, producing fine photographs of seaside resorts and beauty spots that were keenly bought by millions of Victorians. These prints were painstakingly pasted into family albums and pored over during the dark nights of winter, rekindling precious memories of summer excursions.

THE RISE OF FRITH & CO

Frith's studio was soon supplying retail shops all over the country. To meet the demand he gathered about him a small team of photographers, and published the work of independent artist-photographers of the calibre of Roger Fenton and Francis Bedford. In order to gain some understanding of the scale of Frith's business one only has to look at the catalogue issued by Frith & Co in 1886: it runs to some 670 pages, listing not only many thousands of views of the

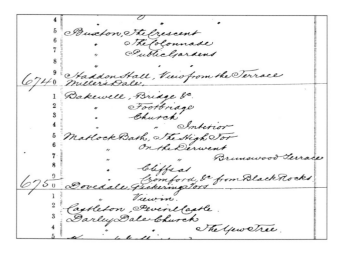

British Isles but also many photographs of most European countries, and China, Japan, the USA and Canada - note the sample page shown here from the hand-written Frith & Co ledgers recording the pictures. By 1890 Frith had created the greatest specialist photographic publishing company in the world, with over 2,000 sales outlets - more than the combined number that Boots and WH Smith have today! The picture above shows the Frith & Co display board at Ingleton in the Yorkshire Dales. Beautifully constructed with mahogany frame and gilt inserts, it could display up to a dozen local scenes.

POSTCARD BONANZA

The ever-popular holiday postcard we know today took many years to develop. In 1870 the Post Office issued the first plain cards, with a pre-printed stamp on one face. In 1894 they allowed other publishers' cards to be sent through the mail with an attached adhesive halfpenny stamp. Demand grew rapidly, and in 1895 a new size of postcard was permitted called the court card, but there was little room for illustration. In 1899, a year after Frith's death, a new card measuring 5.5 x 3.5 inches became the standard format, but it was not until 1902 that the divided back came into being, so that the address and message could be on one face and a full-size illustration on the other. Frith & Co were in the vanguard of postcard development: Frith's sons Eustace and Cyril continued their father's monumental task, expanding the number of views offered to the public and recording more and more places in Britain, as the coasts and countryside were opened up to mass travel.

Francis Frith had died in 1898 at his villa in Cannes, his great project still growing. The archive he created continued in business for another seventy years. By 1970 it contained over a third of a million pictures showing 7,000 British towns and villages.

FRITH'S LEGACY

Francis Frith's legacy to us today is of immense significance and value, for the magnificent archive of evocative photographs he created provides a unique record of change in the cities, towns and villages throughout Britain over a century and more. Frith and his fellow studio photographers revisited locations many times down the years to update their views, compiling for us an enthralling and colourful pageant of British life and character.

We are fortunate that Frith was dedicated to recording the minutiae of everyday life. For it is this sheer wealth of visual data, the painstaking chronicle of changes in dress, transport, street layouts, buildings, housing, engineering and landscape that captivates us so much today. His remarkable images offer us a powerful link with the past and with the lives of our ancestors.

THE VALUE OF THE ARCHIVE TODAY

Computers have now made it possible for Frith's many thousands of images to be accessed almost instantly. Frith's images are increasingly used as visual resources, by social historians, by researchers into genealogy and ancestry, by architects and town planners, and by teachers and schoolchildren involved in local history projects.

In addition, the archive offers every one of us an opportunity to examine the places where we and our families have lived and worked down the years. Highly successful in Frith's own era, the archive is now, a century and more on, entering a new phase of popularity.

THE PAST IN TUNE WITH THE FUTURE

Historians consider the Francis Frith Collection to be of prime national importance. It is the only archive of its kind remaining in private ownership. Francis Frith's archive is now housed in an historic timber barn in the beautiful village of Teffont in Wiltshire. Its founder would not recognize the archive office as it is today. In place of the many thousands of dusty boxes containing glass plate negatives and an all-pervading odour of photographic chemicals, there are now ranks of computer screens. He would be amazed to watch his images travelling round the world at unimaginable speeds through internet lines.

The archive's future is both bright and exciting. Francis Frith, with his unshakeable belief in making photographs available to the greatest number of people, would undoubtedly approve of what is being done today with his lifetime's work. His photographs depicting our shared past are now bringing pleasure and enlightenment to millions around the world a century and more after his death.

Important Telephone Numbers

Doctor	Builder
Dentist	Taxi
Hospital	Bus Station
Police	Rail Enquiries
School	Airport
School	Garage
College	Vet
Babysitter	Bank
Gas	Accountant
Electricity	Solicitor
Water	Credit Card Helpline
Plumber	Post Office
Electrician	Swimming Pool

Family Telephone Numbers

Name   *Name*

Name   *Name*

Name   *Name*

Name   *Name*

Name   *Name*

Name   *Name*

Name   *Name*

Name   *Name*

Name   *Name*

Name   *Name*

Name   *Name*

Name   *Name*

Name   *Name*

Family Telephone Numbers

Name

Name

Name

Name

Name

Name

Name

Name

Name

Name

Name

Name

Name

Name

Name

Name

Name

Name

Name

Name

Name

Name

Name

Name

Name

Name

SHROPSHIRE, MARKET DRAYTON, MARKET DAY 1911 63338

Market Drayton's weekly Wednesday market is still famous in Shropshire, drawing people from all over the county. The region has always been renowned for its dairy products, and in this market scene we see the traders and farmers' wives, many of whom would have been up since dawn, filling their carts with cheeses, home-made jams, marmalades, and fresh-picked cabbages and cucumbers. Here the bustling scene is enlivened by ladies in their extravagant, be-ribboned hats. Note Cushing's lavish display of goods on the right.

A

Name

Address

Phone(s)

Name

Address

Phone(s)

Name

Address

Phone(s)

Name

Address

Phone(s)

Name

Address

Phone(s)

Name

Address

Phone(s)

Name

Address

Phone(s)

BRISTOL, CLIFTON SUSPENSION BRIDGE 1900 45555

Name

Address

Phone(s)

Name

Address

Phone(s)

Name

Address

Phone(s)

Name

Address

Phone(s)

Name

Address

Phone(s)

Name

Address

Phone(s)

Name

Address

Phone(s)

BERKSHIRE, WINDSOR, CASTLE HILL 1914 66981

A

Name

Address

Phone(s)

Name

Address

Phone(s)

Name

Address

Phone(s)

Name

Address

Phone(s)

Name

Address

Phone(s)

Name

Address

Phone(s)

Name

Address

Phone(s)

Name

Address

Phone(s)

CLWYD, RHYL, THE SANDS 1891 29151

Donkeys are awaiting the arrival of the day's holidaymakers on the beach.
A fisherwoman in a tall hat watches from behind the donkey boys and their
mounts. She would wander the sands hawking freshly-caught cockles and
other shell-fish to the visitors. In the background is the pier, which was built
in 1867 at a cost of £23,000.

Rhyl is famous for its great windy expanse of beach facing Liverpool Bay.
The sands were painted with vigour by David Cox in 1854, and were the
inspiration in the 1870s for Gerard Manley Hopkins's beautiful poem ' The
Sea and the Skylark'.

B

Name	*Name*
Address	*Address*
Phone(s)	*Phone(s)*
Name	*Name*
Address	*Address*
Phone(s)	*Phone(s)*
Name	*Name*
Address	*Address*
Phone(s)	*Phone(s)*
Name	*Name*
Address	*Address*
Phone(s)	*Phone(s)*

CHESHIRE, ECCLESTON, THE FERRY c1886 1722

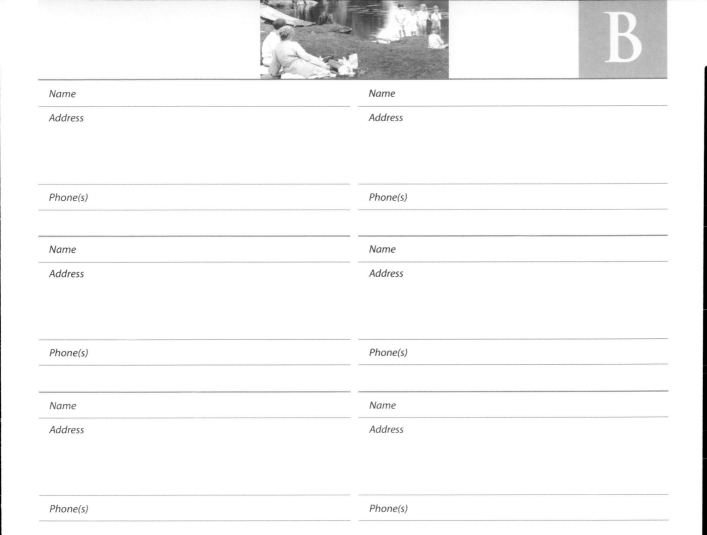

B

Name

Address

Phone(s)

Name

Address

Phone(s)

Name

Address

Phone(s)

Name

Address

Phone(s)

Name

Address

Phone(s)

Name

Address

Phone(s)

B

Name	*Name*
Address	*Address*
Phone(s)	*Phone(s)*
Name	*Name*
Address	*Address*
Phone(s)	*Phone(s)*
Name	*Name*
Address	*Address*
Phone(s)	*Phone(s)*
	Name
	Address
	Phone(s)

CLEVELAND, GUISBOROUGH, MARKET PLACE 1907 58660

Name

Address

Phone(s)

Name

Address

Phone(s)

Name

Address

Phone(s)

Name

Address

Phone(s)

Name

Address

Phone(s)

Name

Address

Phone(s)

Name

Address

Phone(s)

CORNWALL, CHARLESTOWN, THE HARBOUR c1885 16771

B

Name

Address

Phone(s)

Name

Address

Phone(s)

Name

Address

Phone(s)

Name

Address

Phone(s)

Name

Address

Phone(s)

Name

Address

Phone(s)

Name

Address

Phone(s)

Name

Address

Phone(s)

HAMPSHIRE, EVERSLEY, THE WHITE HART 1906   57011

The White Hart was built as a small farmhouse around 1648. It was
not until 1740 that it had earned a reputation as an inn.

The late 19th and early 20th centuries were times of immense
social change in both town and country. Machines had taken over
the manufacture of many household gadgets that had previously
been made by local craftsmen. This mechanisation caused terrible
unemployment. Many older tradesmen, such as the cutler here, were
unable to find work, and took to the streets and lanes with their
handcarts.

C

Name	*Name*
Address	*Address*
Phone(s)	*Phone(s)*
Name	*Name*
Address	*Address*
Phone(s)	*Phone(s)*
Name	*Name*
Address	*Address*
Phone(s)	*Phone(s)*
Name	*Name*
Address	*Address*
Phone(s)	*Phone(s)*

CUMBRIA, AMBLESIDE, THE STEPPING STONES 1888 20484

C

Name

Address

Phone(s)

Name

Address

Phone(s)

Name

Address

Phone(s)

Name

Address

Phone(s)

Name

Address

Phone(s)

Name

Address

Phone(s)

C

Name

Address

Phone(s)

Name

Address

Phone(s)

Name

Address

Phone(s)

Name

Address

Phone(s)

Name

Address

Phone(s)

Name

Address

Phone(s)

Name

Address

Phone(s)

DERBYSHIRE, CASTLETON, SPEEDWELL CAVERN 1909 61785

Name

Address

Phone(s)

Name

Address

Phone(s)

Name

Address

Phone(s)

Name

Address

Phone(s)

Name

Address

Phone(s)

Name

Address

Phone(s)

Name

Address

Phone(s)

BUCKINGHAMSHIRE, AYLESBURY 1901 47462

C

Name	*Name*
Address	*Address*
Phone(s)	*Phone(s)*
Name	*Name*
Address	*Address*
Phone(s)	*Phone(s)*
Name	*Name*
Address	*Address*
Phone(s)	*Phone(s)*
Name	*Name*
Address	*Address*
Phone(s)	*Phone(s)*

NORFOLK, HORNING, THE BROADS 1902 48108

When operating a wherry you had to be able to sail very close to the wind, for the narrow waterways of the Broads allowed no extravagant tacking manoeuvres. It was unwise to touch bottom either, especially when the boat was low in the water and loaded with freight.

Built of East Anglian oak, the gaff-rigged wherry was precisely designed for Broadland conditions, and fleets of them once plied the waters between Yarmouth and Norwich.

D

Name

Address

Phone(s)

Name

Address

Phone(s)

Name

Address

Phone(s)

Name

Address

Phone(s)

Name

Address

Phone(s)

Name

Address

Phone(s)

Name

Address

Phone(s)

DURHAM, BISHOP AUCKLAND, NEWGATE STREET 1914 67136

Name

Address

Phone(s)

Name

Address

Phone(s)

Name

Address

Phone(s)

Name

Address

Phone(s)

Name

Address

Phone(s)

Name

Address

Phone(s)

Name

Address

Phone(s)

DYFED, TENBY, FISH WIVES 1890 28091

D

Name

Address

Phone(s)

Name

Address

Phone(s)

Name

Address

Phone(s)

Name

Address

Phone(s)

Name

Address

Phone(s)

Name

Address

Phone(s)

Name

Address

Phone(s)

Name

Address

Phone(s)

KENT, GOUDHURST, MEASURING THE HOPS 1904 52571

Kent is renowned for the growing of hops. At harvest, farmers hired armies of Londoners to gather the crop, who travelled out by train and waggon to enjoy a few weeks of healthy open-air labour.

Despite the hard work, hopping must have seemed like paradise after the smoke and pollution of the city, with the sun streaming down and the fresh country smells and greenery. Here, a gang of pickers pose in the dappled shade. The hops are being measured before being loaded into a poke, a loose sack that held up to ten bushels - the tallyman with his record book can be seen on the right.

E

Name

Address

Phone(s)

Name

Address

Phone(s)

Name

Address

Phone(s)

Name

Address

Phone(s)

Name

Address

Phone(s)

Name

Address

Phone(s)

CAMBRIDGESHIRE, CAMBRIDGE, PETTY CURY 1909 61469

E

Name

Address

Phone(s)

Name

Address

Phone(s)

Name

Address

Phone(s)

Name

Address

Phone(s)

Name

Address

Phone(s)

Name

Address

Phone(s)

Name

Address

Phone(s)

BRISTOL, THE QUAY 1887 20133

E

Name

Address

Phone(s)

Name

Address

Phone(s)

Name

Address

Phone(s)

Name

Address

Phone(s)

Name

Address

Phone(s)

Name

Address

Phone(s)

Name

Address

Phone(s)

Name

Address

Phone(s)

ISLE OF WIGHT, SHANKLIN, THE COACHES 1913 66211A

There was a great revival of horse-drawn coaches in the late 19th century,
particularly for carrying parties of visitors and holidaymakers on excursions to
local beauty spots. It must have needed considerable courage (or plain blind
trust) for these passengers to sit so precariously high on the coach as it
bounced and swayed along the uneven roads and lanes.

Shanklin was admired by many poets, including John Keats, who wrote
'Lamia' here. Longfellow wrote in praise of the ferruginous spring which
flows out of the Chine - its waters were favoured by health-conscious visitors.

F

Name

Address

Phone(s)

Name

Address

Phone(s)

Name

Address

Phone(s)

Name

Address

Phone(s)

Name

Address

Phone(s)

Name

Address

Phone(s)

Name

Address

Phone(s)

CLEVELAND, REDCAR, THE ESPLANADE 1886 18131

Name

Address

Phone(s)

Name

Address

Phone(s)

Name

Address

Phone(s)

Name

Address

Phone(s)

Name

Address

Phone(s)

Name

Address

Phone(s)

Name

Address

Phone(s)

CORNWALL, NEWQUAY, THE HARBOUR 1894 33522

F

Name

Address

Phone(s)

Name

Address

Phone(s)

Name

Address

Phone(s)

Name

Address

Phone(s)

Name

Address

Phone(s)

Name

Address

Phone(s)

Name

Address

Phone(s)

Name

Address

Phone(s)

NORFOLK, KINGS LYNN, HIGH STREET 1908 60023

Jermyn and Perry's broad shop front dominates this busy High Street scene.
Their display is spectacular, with hats, parasols, curtains and bolts of cloth
tumbling out on to the pavement in a visual feast. It would surely have
required a staff of full-time window-dressers to maintain. The business was
later taken over by Debenham's.

Outside, a young lad pushes his baby sister around in what looks like an
orange box on wheels.

G

Name

Address

Phone(s)

Name

Address

Phone(s)

Name

Address

Phone(s)

Name

Address

Phone(s)

Name

Address

Phone(s)

Name

Address

Phone(s)

Name

Address

Phone(s)

DEVON, COUNTISBURY HILL 1907 59405

G

Name

Address

Phone(s)

Name

Address

Phone(s)

Name

Address

Phone(s)

Name

Address

Phone(s)

Name

Address

Phone(s)

Name

Address

Phone(s)

Name

Address

Phone(s)

JERSEY, ST HELIER, THE HARBOUR 1893 31629

G

Name

Address

Phone(s)

Name

Address

Phone(s)

Name

Address

Phone(s)

Name

Address

Phone(s)

Name

Address

Phone(s)

Name

Address

Phone(s)

Name

Address

Phone(s)

Name

Address

Phone(s)

DEVON, HIGHER CLOVELLY, THE POSTMEN 1936 87551

Outside the post office at Higher Clovelly, postman Roy Fisher accepts the sacks of local post from the Bideford van. Beside him stands the post donkey, who was vital to the efficient and regular deliveries to this isolated North Devon village. Clovelly had no roads, only flights of steep, cobbled steps down which the villagers used donkeys and sleds to carry goods to and from their cottages.

The people of Clovelly had Queen Victoria to thank for their daily post: in 1897, to mark her Golden Jubilee, she extended the right of delivery to every household in Britain.

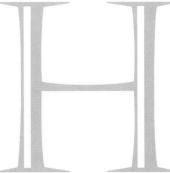

H

Name

Address

Phone(s)

Name

Address

Phone(s)

Name

Address

Phone(s)

Name

Address

Phone(s)

Name

Address

Phone(s)

Name

Address

Phone(s)

Name

Address

Phone(s)

YORKSHIRE, BAINBRIDGE, THE VILLAGE 1889 21661

Name

Address

Phone(s)

Name

Address

Phone(s)

Name

Address

Phone(s)

Name

Address

Phone(s)

Name

Address

Phone(s)

Name

Address

Phone(s)

Name

Address

Phone(s)

GLOUCESTERSHIRE, CHALFORD, THE VILLAGE 1910 62713

H

Name

Address

Phone(s)

Name

Address

Phone(s)

Name

Address

Phone(s)

Name

Address

Phone(s)

Name

Address

Phone(s)

Name

Address

Phone(s)

Name

Address

Phone(s)

Name

Address

Phone(s)

SUSSEX, EASTBOURNE, THE PIER 1925 77946

Charabancs are touting for business at the entrance to Eastbourne pier. The
nearest is bound for Pevensey Bay, where the passengers will tour the castle
ruins and marvel at the Martello towers.

Meanwhile, passengers in the other coach will be enjoying the fresh air of
the South Downs, those with strong stomachs peering dizzily down from
Beachy Head at the matchstick-sized lighthouse hundreds of feet below.
Then, holding their hats firmly on with both hands, they will be up and
over the downs, heading back to Eastbourne and a welcome cream tea.

I J

Name	*Name*
Address	*Address*
Phone(s)	*Phone(s)*
Name	*Name*
Address	*Address*
Phone(s)	*Phone(s)*
Name	*Name*
Address	*Address*
Phone(s)	*Phone(s)*
	Name
	Address
	Phone(s)

ESSEX, CHELMSFORD, HIGH STREET 1898 41504

IJ

Name

Name

Address

Address

Phone(s)

Phone(s)

Name

Name

Address

Address

Phone(s)

Phone(s)

Name

Name

Address

Address

Phone(s)

Phone(s)

Name

Address

Phone(s)

DEVON, PLYMOUTH, THE BARBICAN 1890 22474

IJ

Name	*Name*
Address	*Address*
Phone(s)	*Phone(s)*
Name	*Name*
Address	*Address*
Phone(s)	*Phone(s)*
Name	*Name*
Address	*Address*
Phone(s)	*Phone(s)*
Name	*Name*
Address	*Address*
Phone(s)	*Phone(s)*

SUSSEX, BOGNOR REGIS, THE BEACH 1898 42584

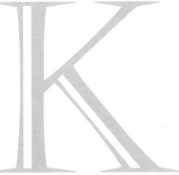

Up until the 1920s, the Bognor bathing machines were ready for business as early as 6am. A contemporary guide book describes how they were 'drawn (by a horse) to any depth required. At low water the bather may even go as far as the rocks; the ladies will find a female guide'. In the foreground is one of the horses whose job it was to haul the heavy bathing machines in and out of the sea.

Beyond the Carlton Hotel on the left, the white wall is the end of Colebrooke Buildings, a crescent of four elegant Regency villas, built in 1826.

K

Name

Address

Phone(s)

Name

Address

Phone(s)

Name

Address

Phone(s)

Name

Address

Phone(s)

Name

Address

Phone(s)

Name

Address

Phone(s)

GRAMPIAN, BRAEMAR, CAIRNWELL 1879 B266003

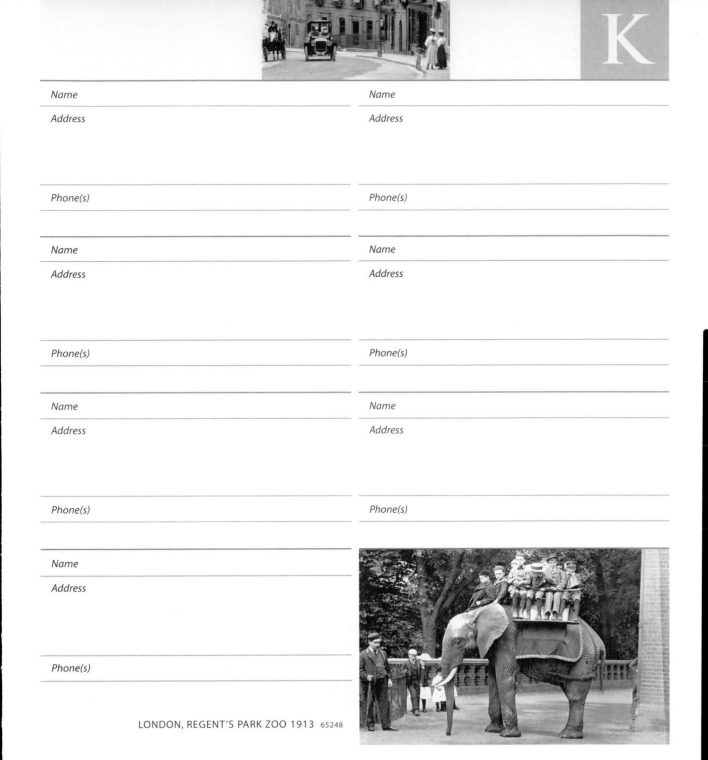

K

Name

Address

Phone(s)

Name

Address

Phone(s)

Name

Address

Phone(s)

Name

Address

Phone(s)

Name

Address

Phone(s)

Name

Address

Phone(s)

LONDON, REGENT'S PARK ZOO 1913 65248

K

Name

Address

Phone(s)

Name

Address

Phone(s)

Name

Address

Phone(s)

Name

Address

Phone(s)

Name

Address

Phone(s)

Name

Address

Phone(s)

Name

Address

Phone(s)

Name

Address

Phone(s)

CUMBRIA, NEWBY BRIDGE 1914 67414

A group of children enjoy a boating trip on the River Leven at Newby Bridge, at the southern end of Lake Windermere. In the background is the 16th-century five-arched stone bridge which gave the village its name, and behind it the Swan Hotel, where trippers for the Lake District caught excursion coaches.

The reflections in the water create a harmonious and peaceful scene. However, things were to change for these children within a month or two: at the end of the summer of 1914 the Great War broke out, and their father would have been called up to join Kitchener's army.

L

Name

Address

Phone(s)

Name

Address

Phone(s)

Name

Address

Phone(s)

Name

Address

Phone(s)

Name

Address

Phone(s)

Name

Address

Phone(s)

Name

Address

Phone(s)

Name

Address

Phone(s)

GWYNEDD, LLANDUDNO 1890 23250

Name
_____

Address
_____

_____

Phone(s)
_____

Name
_____

Address
_____

_____

Phone(s)
_____

Name
_____

Address
_____

_____

Phone(s)
_____

Name
_____

Address
_____

_____

Phone(s)
_____

Name
_____

Address
_____

_____

Phone(s)
_____

Name
_____

Address
_____

_____

Phone(s)
_____

L

Name

Address

Phone(s)

Name

Address

Phone(s)

Name

Address

Phone(s)

Name

Address

Phone(s)

Name

Address

Phone(s)

Name

Address

Phone(s)

Name

Address

Phone(s)

WORCESTERSHIRE, EVESHAM, BRIDGE STREET 1892 31106

Name

Address

Phone(s)

Name

Address

Phone(s)

Name

Address

Phone(s)

Name

Address

Phone(s)

Name

Address

Phone(s)

Name

Address

Phone(s)

ISLE OF MAN, DOUGLAS, THE PROMENADE 1897 39882

L

Name

Address

Phone(s)

Name

Address

Phone(s)

Name

Address

Phone(s)

Name

Address

Phone(s)

Name

Address

Phone(s)

Name

Address

Phone(s)

Name

Address

Phone(s)

Name

Address

Phone(s)

YORKSHIRE, BOLTON ABBEY c1886 18510

Amidst a picturesque setting of meadows and woodland, a young woman
watches her husband painting a watercolour.

Landseer and Turner are just two of the many painters who have been
drawn to the sublime scenery around Bolton Abbey. Photographers, too, have
found it irresistible - Francis Frith exposed fifty glass plates here
during a single visit. The locality is rich in prospects for the artistic eye:
there are the stepping stones across the tumbling River Wharfe, the deep
green hanging woods, and the ancient stones of the ruined 14th-century
chancel.

M

Name

Address

Phone(s)

Name

Address

Phone(s)

Name

Address

Phone(s)

Name

Address

Phone(s)

Name

Address

Phone(s)

Name

Address

Phone(s)

Name

Address

Phone(s)

Name

Address

Phone(s)

KENT, DEAL, THE ESPLANADE 1899 44208

Name	*Name*
Address	*Address*
Phone(s)	*Phone(s)*
Name	*Name*
Address	*Address*
Phone(s)	*Phone(s)*
Name	*Name*
Address	*Address*
Phone(s)	*Phone(s)*

M

Name

Address

Phone(s)

Name

Address

Phone(s)

Name

Address

Phone(s)

Name

Address

Phone(s)

Name

Address

Phone(s)

Name

Address

Phone(s)

Name

Address

Phone(s)

LONDON, PICCADILLY CIRCUS 1886 L130186

Name	*Name*
Address	*Address*
Phone(s)	*Phone(s)*
Name	*Name*
Address	*Address*
Phone(s)	*Phone(s)*
Name	*Name*
Address	*Address*
Phone(s)	*Phone(s)*
Name	
Address	
Phone(s)	

GTR MANCHESTER, BOWDON, STAMFORD ROAD 1907 58602

M

Name

Address

Phone(s)

Name

Address

Phone(s)

Name

Address

Phone(s)

Name

Address

Phone(s)

Name

Address

Phone(s)

Name

Address

Phone(s)

Name

Address

Phone(s)

Name

Address

Phone(s)

DORSET, BOURNEMOUTH, INVALIDS' WALK 1900 45226

Bournemouth developed late as a seaside resort. However, it gained a reputation in the early part of the 19th century as a place of convalescence, its 'warm and sheltered locality' and balmy climate being perfect for those suffering from consumptive diseases. This charming pinewood walk near the Westover Road soon became known as Invalids' Walk, and was part of the town's pleasure gardens. The scented pines and attractively laid out grounds were popular with the aged and sick for whiling away a quiet afternoon.

N

Name

Address

Phone(s)

Name

Address

Phone(s)

Name

Address

Phone(s)

Name

Address

Phone(s)

Name

Address

Phone(s)

Name

Address

Phone(s)

Name

Address

Phone(s)

GWYNEDD, CRICCIETH, THE GOLF CLUB 1913 65789

Name

Address

Phone(s)

Name

Address

Phone(s)

Name

Address

Phone(s)

Name

Address

Phone(s)

Name

Address

Phone(s)

Name

Address

Phone(s)

Name

Address

Phone(s)

ALTRINCHAM, RAILWAY STREET 1907 58604

N

Name

Address

Phone(s)

Name

Address

Phone(s)

Name

Address

Phone(s)

Name

Address

Phone(s)

Name

Address

Phone(s)

Name

Address

Phone(s)

Name

Address

Phone(s)

Name

Address

Phone(s)

DUMFRIES AND GALLOWAY, MOFFAT, A TENNIS MATCH 1892 M113003

At the beginning of the 20th century, Moffat attracted considerable numbers of tourists wishing to sample the curative waters of the nearby sulphureous-saline wells. It was around this time that tennis became popular, with many spa towns hosting annual tournaments.

Here, a mixed doubles match is under way. The ladies, as in all Victorian sports, are at a considerable disadvantage with their long, billowing dresses and broad-brimmed hats. They were only allowed to serve under-arm, and lobbing was unheard of.

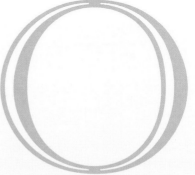

O

Name

Address

Phone(s)

Name

Address

Phone(s)

Name

Address

Phone(s)

Name

Address

Phone(s)

Name

Address

Phone(s)

Name

Address

Phone(s)

DYFED, TENBY, THE HARBOUR 1890 28041

Name

Address

Phone(s)

Name

Address

Phone(s)

Name

Address

Phone(s)

Name

Address

Phone(s)

Name

Address

Phone(s)

Name

Address

Phone(s)

Name

Address

Phone(s)

LEICESTERSHIRE, MELTON MOWBRAY 1932 85169

O

Name

Address

Phone(s)

Name

Address

Phone(s)

Name

Address

Phone(s)

Name

Address

Phone(s)

Name

Address

Phone(s)

Name

Address

Phone(s)

Name

Address

Phone(s)

Name

Address

Phone(s)

ESSEX, SAFFRON WALDEN, THE MAZE 1907 58821

They have made it! The two weary explorers rest after battling their way to the centre of the maze in Bridge End Gardens. The head gardener looks on with a wicked grin - he has already charged them 6d to get into the maze. If he was feeling just a little bit unscrupulous he could charge them another 6d to get out.

This superb Victorian yew hedge maze was laid out and planted in the Italianate style by Francis Gibson in the 1840s. The two thousand feet of narrow, close-clipped paths were decorated with a Chinese pavilion and much ornate statuary.

P

Name

Address

Phone(s)

Name

Address

Phone(s)

Name

Address

Phone(s)

Name

Address

Phone(s)

Name

Address

Phone(s)

Name

Address

Phone(s)

Name

Address

Phone(s)

Name

Address

Phone(s)

MERSEYSIDE, NEW BRIGHTON, THE BEACH 1887 20067

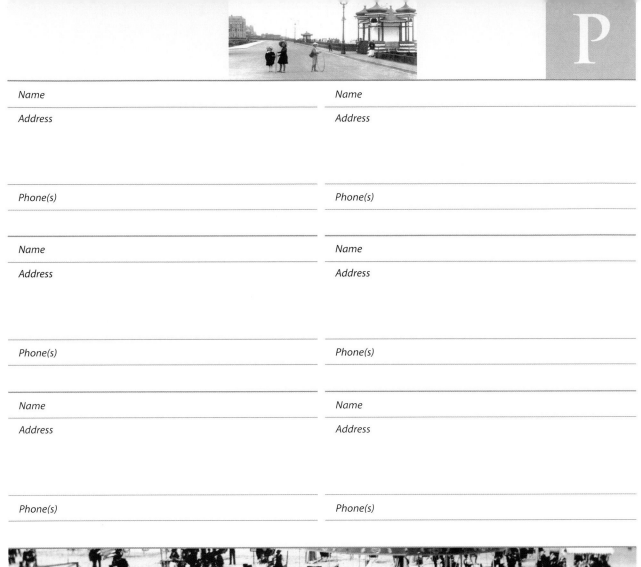

Name
_____

Address
_____

Phone(s)
_____

Name
_____

Address
_____

Phone(s)
_____

Name
_____

Address
_____

Phone(s)
_____

Name
_____

Address
_____

Phone(s)
_____

Name
_____

Address
_____

Phone(s)
_____

Name
_____

Address
_____

Phone(s)
_____

P

Name

Address

Phone(s)

Name

Address

Phone(s)

Name

Address

Phone(s)

Name

Address

Phone(s)

Name

Address

Phone(s)

Name

Address

Phone(s)

Name

Address

Phone(s)

LONDON, MUSWELL HILL 1910 M298365

Name

Address

Phone(s)

Name

Address

Phone(s)

Name

Address

Phone(s)

Name

Address

Phone(s)

Name

Address

Phone(s)

Name

Address

Phone(s)

Name

Address

Phone(s)

KENT, RAMSGATE, THE HARBOUR 1901   48028

P

Name

Address

Phone(s)

Name

Address

Phone(s)

Name

Address

Phone(s)

Name

Address

Phone(s)

Name

Address

Phone(s)

Name

Address

Phone(s)

Name

Address

Phone(s)

Name

Address

Phone(s)

DORSET, WEYMOUTH, THE SANDS 1909 61597

Weymouth was one of the earliest holiday resorts on England's southern coast. An old guidebook praised it fulsomely: 'It is much more open than the majority of seaside resorts, and is almost surrounded by salt water. This results in an air largely impregnated with ozone and, with the ever-changing tide, ensures a constantly renewed atmosphere'.

Here, children, their skirts bunched up, are paddling in the shallows. Visitors would have paid 63 shillings to stay full board at one of the town's better hotels, and about 8 shillings at one of the cheapest.

Q

Q

Name	*Name*
Address	*Address*
Phone(s)	*Phone(s)*
Name	*Name*
Address	*Address*
Phone(s)	*Phone(s)*
Name	*Name*
Address	*Address*
Phone(s)	*Phone(s)*

Name

Address

Phone(s)

LINCOLNSHIRE, LINCOLN, STONEBOW 1906 55113

Q

Name	Name
Address	Address
Phone(s)	Phone(s)
Name	Name
Address	Address
Phone(s)	Phone(s)
Name	Name
Address	Address
Phone(s)	Phone(s)
Name	
Address	

Phone(s)

EDINBURGH, THE BLACK WATCH AT THE CASTLE 1897 39121A

Q

Name

Address

Phone(s)

Name

Address

Phone(s)

Name

Address

Phone(s)

Name

Address

Phone(s)

Name

Address

Phone(s)

Name

Address

Phone(s)

Name

Address

Phone(s)

Name

Address

Phone(s)

LONDON, GREENWICH, A HOKEY POKEY STALL 1884 L130110

Children cluster round licking the cheap ice cream from the hokey pokey stall. They look like ragged street urchins in their rumpled suits and battered boots, and were probably bought their treats by the Frith photographer in return for posing.

Life was a constant struggle for the poor, and young children often worked as match sellers, shoe blacks and flower girls. Many who had been born in the country moved to the cities in the hope of a better life after the slump in farming. There was, of course, no social relief, and families were forced to rely on their native guile to keep body and soul together.

R

R

Name

Address

Phone(s)

Name

Address

Phone(s)

Name

Address

Phone(s)

Name

Address

Phone(s)

Name

Address

Phone(s)

Name

Address

Phone(s)

Name

Address

Phone(s)

Name

Address

Phone(s)

NORTHAMPTONSHIRE, KETTERING, THE MARKET 1922 72232

Name

Address

Phone(s)

Name

Address

Phone(s)

Name

Address

Phone(s)

Name

Address

Phone(s)

Name

Address

Phone(s)

Name

Address

Phone(s)

R

Name	*Name*
Address	*Address*
Phone(s)	*Phone(s)*
Name	*Name*
Address	*Address*
Phone(s)	*Phone(s)*
Name	*Name*
Address	*Address*
Phone(s)	*Phone(s)*
	Name
	Address
	Phone(s)

LIVERPOOL, GEORGE'S DOCK c1881 14149

Name

Address

Phone(s)

Name

Address

Phone(s)

Name

Address

Phone(s)

Name

Address

Phone(s)

Name

Address

Phone(s)

Name

Address

Phone(s)

Name

Address

Phone(s)

BELFAST, CASTLE PLACE 1897 40187A

R

Name	*Name*
Address	*Address*
Phone(s)	*Phone(s)*
Name	*Name*
Address	*Address*
Phone(s)	*Phone(s)*
Name	*Name*
Address	*Address*
Phone(s)	*Phone(s)*
Name	*Name*
Address	*Address*
Phone(s)	*Phone(s)*

DORSET, LYME REGIS, THE SMITHY 1909 61633A

The painter J M Whistler visited Lyme in 1895. As he climbed the steep
main street he must have heard Samuel Govier's hammer crashing against iron
in his smithy, and seen the glowing fire and the shower of incandescent
sparks through the dim doorway. Captivated, he set to and painted 'The
Master Smith of Lyme Regis'.

A painting by a famous artist is no guarantee of immortality, however.
In Lyme today nothing of Govier's smithy remains, and a supermarket covers
his old yard. We are lucky to have this superb Frith photograph as a record.

S

Name

Address

Phone(s)

Name

Address

Phone(s)

Name

Address

Phone(s)

Name

Address

Phone(s)

Name

Address

Phone(s)

Name

Address

Phone(s)

Name

Address

Phone(s)

Name

Address

Phone(s)

NOTTINGHAM, WHEELER GATE 1902 48327

Name

Name

Address

Address

Phone(s)

Phone(s)

Name

Name

Address

Address

Phone(s)

Phone(s)

Name

Name

Address

Address

Phone(s)

Phone(s)

S

Name

Address

Phone(s)

Name

Address

Phone(s)

Name

Address

Phone(s)

Name

Address

Phone(s)

Name

Address

Phone(s)

Name

Address

Phone(s)

Name

Address

Phone(s)

OXFORDSHIRE, IFFLEY, THE MILL AND LOCK 1890 26959

Name

Address

Phone(s)

Name

Address

Phone(s)

Name

Address

Phone(s)

Name

Address

Phone(s)

Name

Address

Phone(s)

Name

Address

Phone(s)

Name

Address

Phone(s)

YORKSHIRE, ALDBOROUGH, THE VILLAGE 1907 58636

S

Name

Address

Phone(s)

Name

Address

Phone(s)

Name

Address

Phone(s)

Name

Address

Phone(s)

Name

Address

Phone(s)

Name

Address

Phone(s)

Name

Address

Phone(s)

Name

Address

Phone(s)

YORKSHIRE, SANDSEND, EAST ROW 1925 78993

Sandsend was just three miles along the sandy beach from Whitby. It was a popular place for holidays when this picture was taken, even though the village was disfigured by a ruin of an alum works and an iron bridge that carried the LNER railway line from Whitby to Saltburn. The alum mines gave employment until the 1860s, and there are still traces of the workings nearby. To the north of Sandsend lies Kettleness, or rather what is left of it. During a violent storm in 1829, the cliff fell into the sea taking most of Kettleness with it.

T

Name	Name
Address	Address
Phone(s)	Phone(s)
Name	Name
Address	Address
Phone(s)	Phone(s)
Name	Name
Address	Address
Phone(s)	Phone(s)
Name	Name
Address	Address
Phone(s)	Phone(s)

GLASGOW, ST VINCENT PLACE 1897 39764

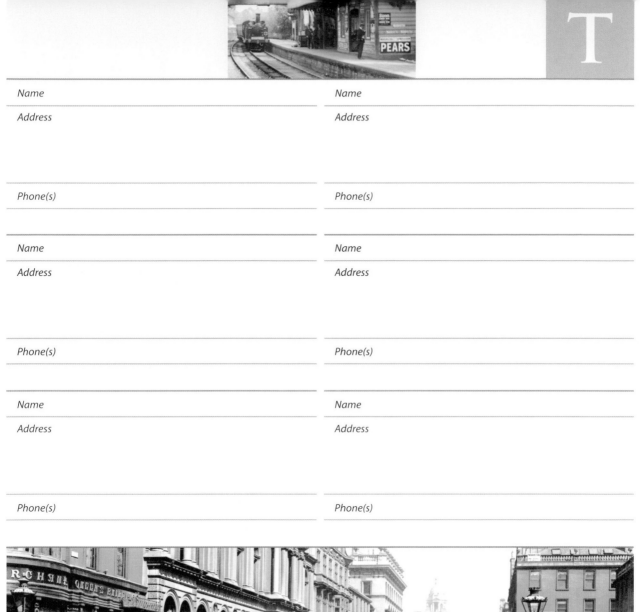

Name	*Name*
Address	*Address*
Phone(s)	*Phone(s)*
Name	*Name*
Address	*Address*
Phone(s)	*Phone(s)*
Name	*Name*
Address	*Address*
Phone(s)	*Phone(s)*

T

Name

Address

Phone(s)

Name

Address

Phone(s)

Name

Address

Phone(s)

Name

Address

Phone(s)

Name

Address

Phone(s)

Name

Address

Phone(s)

Name

Address

Phone(s)

SOMERSET, DULVERTON, THE LION HOTEL 1896 37653

Name

Address

Phone(s)

Name

Address

Phone(s)

Name

Address

Phone(s)

Name

Address

Phone(s)

Name

Address

Phone(s)

Name

Address

Phone(s)

Name

Address

Phone(s)

WARWICKSHIRE, STRATFORD-UPON-AVON,
SHAKESPEARE'S BIRTHPLACE 1861 S21602

T

Name

Address

Phone(s)

Name

Address

Phone(s)

Name

Address

Phone(s)

Name

Address

Phone(s)

Name

Address

Phone(s)

Name

Address

Phone(s)

Name

Address

Phone(s)

Name

Address

Phone(s)

HUMBERSIDE, CLEETHORPES, THE BEACH 1906 55736

Here we have a wonderfully evocative Edwardian holiday scene: the beach in high summer, and not a glimpse of bare arm or leg - casual clothing was almost unknown during this period. Cleethorpes was renowned for its superb pleasure beach, which was popularly known as 'Wonderland'. Its lofty Flying Machine, seen in the background, dominated the sky-line up to the mid-1940s.

The helter-skelter was very popular for its safe but spectacular rides. It survived two world wars, but finally succumbed to the great floods of 1953, which washed the entire seaside amusements away in a single night.

U

U

Name _____

Address _____

Phone(s) _____

Name _____

Address _____

Phone(s) _____

Name _____

Address _____

Phone(s) _____

Name _____

Address _____

Phone(s) _____

Name _____

Address _____

Phone(s) _____

Name _____

Address _____

Phone(s) _____

SOMERSET, DUNSTER, THE MARKET HOUSE c1880 15837

Name

Address

Phone(s)

Name

Address

Phone(s)

Name

Address

Phone(s)

Name

Address

Phone(s)

Name

Address

Phone(s)

Name

Address

Phone(s)

Name

Address

Phone(s)

STAFFORDSHIRE, ECCLESHALL, HIGH STREET 1900 46157

U

Name

Address

Phone(s)

Name

Address

Phone(s)

Name

Address

Phone(s)

Name

Address

Phone(s)

Name

Address

Phone(s)

Name

Address

Phone(s)

Name

Address

Phone(s)

Name

Address

Phone(s)

SURREY, EAST MOLESEY, HOUSEBOATS IN THE LOCK 1896 38350

Luncheon on this steam launch has been consumed by the boating party and
the two housemaids are enjoying a well-earned rest. We can be certain they
needed it, for they would have been up since dawn filling the hampers with
joints of cold roast beef, fowls, duck, ham, veal pie and collared calf's head,
all to be followed by stewed fruit, cabinet pudding and plum cake.

During Ascot week the Thames was thronged with skiffs and launches,
and the scene was a riot of colour and a brilliant tangle of bright blazers,
caps and saucy hats.

V

V

Name

Address

Phone(s)

Name

Address

Phone(s)

Name

Address

Phone(s)

Name

Address

Phone(s)

Name

Address

Phone(s)

Name

Address

Phone(s)

Name

Address

Phone(s)

BARRY ISLAND, PADDLING 1925 77482

Name _____

Address _____

Phone(s) _____

Name _____

Address _____

Phone(s) _____

Name _____

Address _____

Phone(s) _____

Name _____

Address _____

Phone(s) _____

Name _____

Address _____

Phone(s) _____

Name _____

Address _____

Phone(s) _____

LONDON, CRYSTAL PALACE PARK c1890 L130021

V

Name	Name
Address	Address
Phone(s)	Phone(s)

Name	Name
Address	Address
Phone(s)	Phone(s)

Name	Name
Address	Address
Phone(s)	Phone(s)

Name	Name
Address	Address
Phone(s)	Phone(s)

SUSSEX, CRAWLEY, THE MARKET 1905 53326

Here in the broad market place the agricultural sale is in full swing. In the centre, in front of the white house, a hay elevator rises high over the busy scene. In the foreground, farmers in long coats and bowler hats are haggling over the price of horned cattle. An open-topped motor-car, though doubtless a rare sight in the town at the time, threads its way unnoticed between the groups of animals.

Crawley's farmers' market, established in 1902, survives today, but now sells clothes and vegetables rather than livestock.

W

W

Name

Address

Phone(s)

Name

Address

Phone(s)

Name

Address

Phone(s)

Name

Address

Phone(s)

Name

Address

Phone(s)

Name

Address

Phone(s)

WILTSHIRE, MARLBOROUGH, HIGH STREET 1907 57847

Name

Name

Address

Address

Phone(s)

Phone(s)

Name

Name

Address

Address

Phone(s)

Phone(s)

Name

Name

Address

Address

Phone(s)

Phone(s)

W

Name

Address

Phone(s)

Name

Address

Phone(s)

Name

Address

Phone(s)

Name

Address

Phone(s)

Name

Address

Phone(s)

Name

Address

Phone(s)

YORKSHIRE, WHITBY, THE BRIDGE 1913   66266

Name

Address

Phone(s)

Name

Address

Phone(s)

Name

Address

Phone(s)

Name

Address

Phone(s)

Name

Address

Phone(s)

Name

Address

Phone(s)

Name

Address

Phone(s)

NEWCASTLE UPON TYNE, THE QUAYSIDE 1928 N16016

W

Name

Address

Phone(s)

Name

Address

Phone(s)

Name

Address

Phone(s)

Name

Address

Phone(s)

Name

Address

Phone(s)

Name

Address

Phone(s)

Name

Address

Phone(s)

Name

Address

Phone(s)

YORKSHIRE, STAITHES, CHURCH STREET 1925 79004

During the 19th and early 20th centuries, Staithes was a fishing port of some standing, being a centre for cod, haddock and mackerel. However, it fell into decline with the development of steam trawlers, which tended to be concentrated in the larger east coast ports.

   As with other fishing villages along the Yorkshire coast, Staithes clings to the sides of steep cliffs and ravines. The old gentleman could be delivering fresh milk to his neighbours, but during this period yokes were used for carrying all sorts of goods and produce up the steep streets.

XY

XY

XY

Name

Address

Phone(s)

Name

Address

Phone(s)

Name

Address

Phone(s)

Name

Address

Phone(s)

Name

Address

Phone(s)

Name

Address

Phone(s)

Name

Address

Phone(s)

STRATHCLYDE, ARRAN, THE CASTLE c1890 A93001

Name

Address

Phone(s)

Name

Address

Phone(s)

Name

Address

Phone(s)

Name

Address

Phone(s)

Name

Address

Phone(s)

Name

Address

Phone(s)

Name

Address

Phone(s)

W MIDLANDS, WOLVERHAMPTON, DUDLEY ST c1900   W285007

XY

Name	Name
Address	Address
Phone(s)	Phone(s)

Name	Name
Address	Address
Phone(s)	Phone(s)

Name	Name
Address	Address
Phone(s)	Phone(s)

Name	Name
Address	Address
Phone(s)	Phone(s)

HERTFORDSHIRE, CASSIOBURY, THE CANAL LOCK 1921 70492

In this fine old photograph of the Grand Union Canal, the horse on the left is
waiting to haul George Garside's two barges, which are 'breasted up' together
in the lock. The lower regions of the Grand Union waterway were built
especially to accommodate two boats alongside each other.

The lock-keeper sits on the balance beam enjoying a peaceful break.
Ahead the water lies placid and serene, and great trees dip their branches
over the water.

Z

Name

Address

Phone(s)

Name

Address

Phone(s)

Name

Address

Phone(s)

Name

Address

Phone(s)

Name

Address

Phone(s)

Name

Address

Phone(s)

Name

Address

Phone(s)

Name

Address

Phone(s)

As interest in family history and roots grows world-wide,
more and more people are turning to Frith's photographs of
Great Britain for images of the towns, villages and streets where
their ancestors lived.

Any photograph in this address book which is titled and dated
can be ordered as a framed or mounted print - please quote the
unique reference number of the individual photograph.
All other photographs in the Frith archive are also available as
framed or mounted prints. Please order from the address below.
From time to time, other illustrated items such as Cyfeiriad /
Address Books, Calendars and Table Mats are
also available.

The Francis Frith Collection has published over 400 local
history books, each lavishly illustrated with photographs from
the archive. They cover the counties and towns of Britain, as
well as a range of fascinating theme subjects. For a full list,
contact the Collection at the address or phone number below, or
browse the Frith website.

Already, almost 50,000 Frith photographs can be viewed and
purchased on the internet through the Frith
website and a myriad of partner sites.

For more detailed information on Frith companies
and products, visit:

www.francisfrith.co.uk

Or contact:

The Francis Frith Collection,
Frith's Barn, Teffont,
Salisbury, Wiltshire SP3 5QP
Tel: +44 (0) 1722 716 376